The HACKNEY Martian

Written by Paul Brown

Illustrated by Rowena Blyth

fourth wall
publishing

Sam watched as a shooting star
flashed across the evening sky,
but in the blink of an eye it was gone.

Welcome to

HACKNEY
MARSHES

Nothing exciting
ever happens to me.

Out in space, Max the Martian was heading home, when suddenly he found himself in the middle of a meteor shower.

He tried to navigate through the rain of fireballs, when suddenly there was a huge 'BANG!!!' as a meteorite smashed into his little spaceship!

BANG!!!

Thrown into a spin and losing power fast,
Max knew he was in real trouble!

But as he tumbled through space,
he managed to spot a nearby
planet where he could make
an emergency landing.

Max crashed his little spaceship into a large tree.

Feeling slightly **dizzy**, he looked down and spotted a small boy smiling up at him.

Hi I'm Max.

Hello, I'm Sam.

Realising that Max needed
to keep out of sight, Sam helped
his new found friend drag the
spaceship into a nearby tunnel
to carry out repairs.

"Oh no!" cried Max.

"The fuel jewel must have come loose during the meteor storm."

Max explained that his spaceship is powered by diamonds and he must find another if he is ever to return home!

FUEL

B-L-E-E-E-E-E-P!!!

Tower of London
London
EC3N 4AB (5 miles)

Max switched on his diamond detector and located a replacement jewel only five miles away...

"COME ON, LET'S GET IT!" said Max.

"That might be a problem!" explained Sam.

"That diamond is locked away in a huge fortress called the Tower of London."

To reach the jewel, there would be many difficult obstacles to overcome...

PROBLEM 1

DISTRACT THE RAVENS

A large family of ravens patrol the grounds of the Tower to alert the guards of any intruders.

PROBLEM 2

GET PAST THE GUARDS

For hundreds of years, Beefeater guards have protected the Tower both day and night.

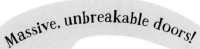

Massive, unbreakable doors!

PROBLEM 3
OPEN THE VAULT DOOR

The diamond is locked away in a huge vault with thick, metal doors.

PROBLEM 5
GET THE DIAMOND

Even the base that the diamond sits on is alarmed!

PROBLEM 4
AVOID THE LASER BEAMS

If they managed to get into the vault, they would have to dodge the laser beams or they would set off the alarm.

Sam and Max quickly formed a plan
and gathered up all the equipment
they would need before setting off
on their quest.

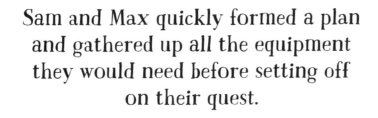

To keep
out of sight,
they journeyed
under the streets
of London, through
a secret network
of old underground
tunnels.

On their travels they came across
all kinds of nasty, horrible things!

The deeper they descended,
the darker it became.

They even had to swim through caverns
filled with murky, smelly water!

Eventually, they met some
friendly rats who pointed
them in the right direction.

Beware
of the
ravens!

IT'S NOT
TOO LATE
TO TURN BACK!

On and on they crawled and
climbed, until they finally reached
the secret entrance to the Tower.

TO THE TOWER
OF LONDON →

B-L-E-E-E-P!!!!

"This is it!"
whispered Max excitedly.
"Now we need to
distract the ravens."

That should
keep them
busy!

Sam used his catapult
to fire handfuls of seed
for the greedy birds.

With the ravens distracted,
they put on their soft,
fluffy slippers and quietly tip-toed
past the sleeping guards.

GUARDS OFFICE
(DO NOT ENTER)

zzzZZZ

zzzZZ

zzzZZZ

SHHHH

They made it to the vault
but the doors were too big and
heavy to open, so Max set his raygun
to silent and zapped through
the thick metal!

Once inside the vault,
they looked down
into the deep chamber
and glimpsed their
shining prize below.

Sam used his special
laser detecting spray
to safely guide them
through the laser beams.

Slowly,
they lowered
themselves...

...down

towards

the

diamond.

Just as Max was about to grab the sparkling gem, Sam spotted a warning...

STOOOPP!!! the jewel is cursed!

BEWARE
THE CURSE OF THE DIAMOND

THIS JEWEL IS SPARKLING,
SHINY AND BRIGHT,
AND MANY DESIRE TO HOLD IT TIGHT.
BUT BE WARNED, ITS POWER IS DOUBLE,
FOR THOSE WHO STEAL IT,
WILL HAVE ONLY
TROUBLE!

INTRUDER ALARM

SQUAWK!!

SQUAWK!!

ER

E R

Sam's shouting sent
Max into a spin and
he triggered the alarm!

All the commotion alerted
the ravens, whose loud squawking
woke up the guards!

The furious ravens gave chase!
Sam and Max ran and ran as fast as their feet
would carry them. By the time they reached the
old well, they were both nearly out of breath.

Back underground, heavy rain
had started to fill the tunnels with water,
making the thick mud very sticky and
difficult to run through.

And the Beefeaters and ravens
started to catch them up!

Just then, a huge wave
hurtled down the tunnel
crashing into everybody!

Luckily for Sam and Max,
it carried them away, leaving the
ravens and Beefeaters far behind...

...until finally, it dumped them right back to where they had started from.

Feeling tired, wet and miserable,
and without the diamond to
power his spaceship,
Max thought he may never
see his family again...

Ta
Dah!

...and Sam wondered
what his Mum would say
when he brought his new friend
home to live with them!

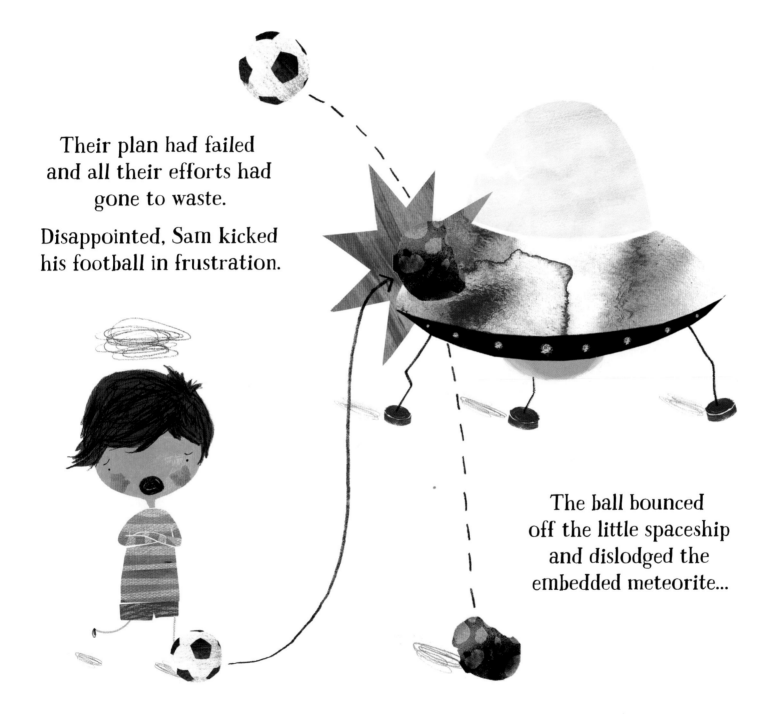

Their plan had failed and all their efforts had gone to waste.

Disappointed, Sam kicked his football in frustration.

The ball bounced off the little spaceship and dislodged the embedded meteorite...

With his spaceship
repaired, Max was finally
ready to fly home.

As he climbed aboard,
Max handed Sam the remaining
diamonds and promised
his new friend he would
return one day.

gone.

he was

of an eye

...and in the blink

All the stars were sparkling,
just like tiny diamonds
as Sam watched his Martian friend
disappear into the night sky...